سميرة في العيد

Samira's Eid

Nasreen Aktar
Illustrated by Enebor Attard

Arabic translation by Azza Habashi

كان الوقت رمضان وكان الكل صائماً، وكان الطفلان
مشغولين بكتابة بطاقات التهنئة بالعيد.
"هذه للجدة في المستشفى" قالت سميرة وهي تغلق الظرف.
سأل حسن: "هل ستتحسن حالتها؟"
"نعم، ولكن العيد لن يكون جميلاً من دونها".

It was during Ramadan, when everybody was fasting, that the children
were busy making cards.
"This one's for Nani in hospital," said Samira, closing the envelope.
"Will she get better?" asked Hassan.
"Yes, but Eid won't be the same without her."

دخلت الأم في الحال وقالت: "تذكرا أنكما صائمين غداً".
"هل سيكون صعباً؟" سأل حسن.
أجابت الأم: "لا بل ستشعر بالتعب. ولذا إذهب ونم بسرعة الآن".

Just then, Mum walked in. "Remember you're fasting tomorrow," she said.
"Will it hurt?" asked Hassan.
"No, but you will feel tired. So go to sleep quickly now," answered Mum.

في الصباح التالي وقبل شروق الشمس، تناول حسن وسميرة سحورهما.
"تناولا كل طعامكما، فإن الوقت طويل حتى وقت الإفطار" ذكرتهما الأم.

The next morning, before sunrise, Samira and Hassan had their breakfast.
"Eat up! It's a long time till dinner," Mum reminded them.

وعندما جاء وقت الغداء لم يستطع حسن ان يمنع نفسه من الشكوى.
"أنا جائع جداً. أريد سمبوسك".
"وأنا جائعة أيضاً، ولكن فكر في الناس الصائمين مثلنا" قالت سميرة.

But by lunch time, Hassan couldn't stop himself complaining,
"I'm sooo hungry. I want a samosa."
"I'm hungry too, but think of all the people who are fasting
just like us," said Samira.

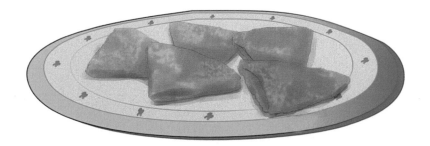

"وفكر كذلك في هؤلاء الناس الذين لا يأكلون سوى وجبة واحدة في اليوم" قالت الأم واضعة ذراعها على كتف حسن.
"أنا لا أحب ذلك" قال حسن.
"حسناً وهم كذلك لا يحبون ذلك". وقالت سميرة: "لذلك ندفع الزكاة".

"And think of all the people who can only have one meal a day," said Mum, putting her arm around Hassan.
"I wouldn't like that," said Hassan.
"Well, they don't like it either," said Samira. "That's why we give zakat."

وأخيراً جاء وقت الإفطار، وكانت الأم قد أعدت أطعمتهما المفضلة.
قالت سميرة لوالدها: "لقد استطعنا ان نصوم مثلكم".
تبسم الأب وقال: "كنت متأكداً من استطاعتكما. كيف تشعران الآن؟"
تأوه الطفلان وقالا: "جائعان".

At last it was time for dinner, and Mum had prepared their favourite food.
"Dad, we did it! We fasted just like you," said Samira.
"I knew you could do it," said Dad, smiling. "How do you feel?"
"Hungry," they groaned.

وفي ليلة العيد أُعلن في الإذاعة رؤية الهلال.
وجرت سميرة بسرعة الى غرفة حسن لتزف
إليه الخبر.

The night before Eid, the radio announced the
sighting of the new moon. Quickly Samira ran
to Hassan's room to tell him the news.

"لقد ظهر الهلال" قالت سميرة.
"أين؟" سأل حسن وأسرع الى النافذة.
"في مكة طبعاً وليس هنا!"

"The new moon has just been seen," she said.
"Where?" asked Hassan, dashing to the window.
"In Mecca of course, not here!"

Very early, while everyone was still asleep, Samira and Hassan gazed at the new moon, so thin and pale in the morning sky.
"Look Hassan, there it is," whispered Samira.
"Eid Mubarak, Samira," said Hassan.

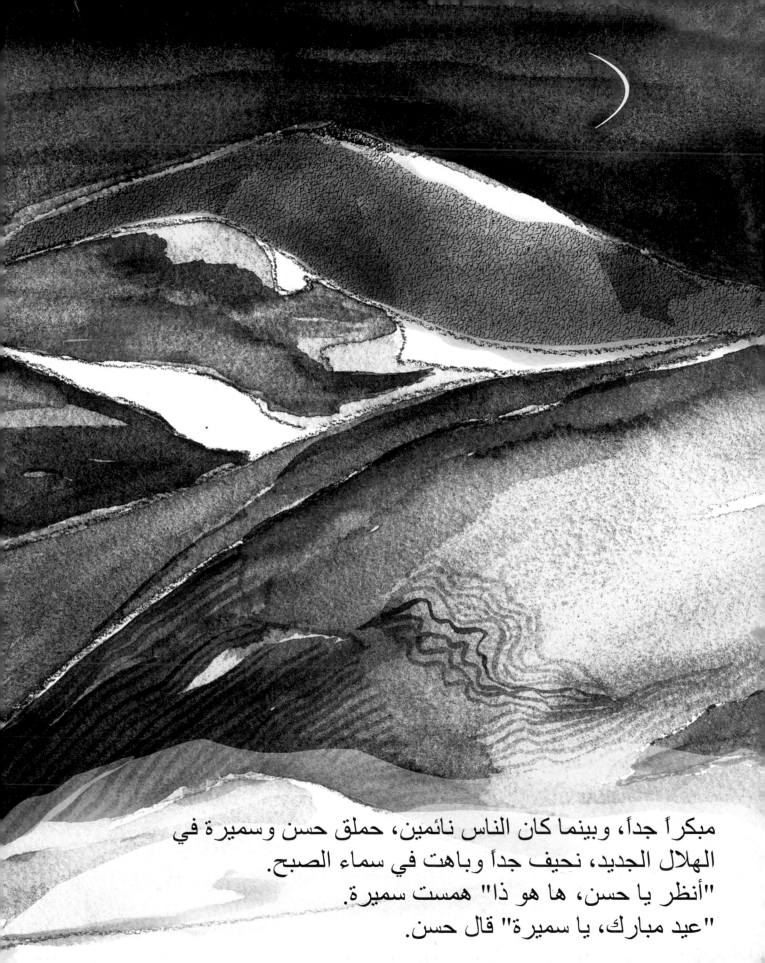

مبكراً جداً، وبينما كان الناس نائمين، حملق حسن وسميرة في الهلال الجديد، نحيف جداً وباهت في سماء الصبح.

"أنظر يا حسن، ها هو ذا" همست سميرة.

"عيد مبارك، يا سميرة" قال حسن.

رجعت سميرة الى غرفتها فوجدت ملابسها الجديدة على سريرها.
وبرفق رفعت القميص الذي صنعته لها أمها إلى أعلى.
وعندئذ أيقنت أنه العيد.

Back in her room, Samira saw her new clothes lying on the bed.
Gently she lifted the shalwar-kameez that her mum had made and held
it up. It really is Eid, she thought.

وعندما تجهز أفراد الأسرة توجهوا الى المسجد مرددين:
"عيد مبارك" لكل اصدقائهم في الطريق.
وداخل المسجد أدوا الصلاة واستمعوا الى الإمام.

When everyone was ready, the family left for the mosque.
"Eid Mubarak," they called out to their friends on the way.
Inside the mosque they prayed and listened to the Imam.

وفي خارج المسجد كانت جموع الناس تبتسم
ويحتضن بعضهم بعضاً. فجأة رأت سميرة معلمتها.
وصاحت: "أنظر يا حسن السيدة قديرة مقبلة علينا".

Outside there were lots of
people smiling and hugging each
other. Suddenly, Samira saw her
teacher. "Look Hassan, it's
Mrs Qadir coming over here."

"عيد مبارك يا سميرة، عيد مبارك يا حسن" قالت السيدة قديرة ووضعت في يد كل منهما هدية.
فشكراها وسألاها: "كيف عرفتِ أننا هنا؟"
تبسمت المعلمة وقالت: "المعلمون يعرفون مثل هذه الأشياء".

"Eid Mubarak, Samira and Hassan," said Mrs Qadir, placing a small present in their hands.
"Thank you," they said. "But how did you know that we'd be here?"
"Teachers know these things," replied Mrs Qadir, smiling.

عندما رجعوا الى البيت وجدوا كومة من المظاريف تنتظر ان تُفتح.
"هذه واحدة من الخالة ياسمين، وهذه من العم إقبال" قالت سميرة.
"ولكن أين كارت الجدة؟"

When they arrived home they found a pile of Eid cards waiting to be opened. "Here's one from Aunty Yasmin, and this one's from Uncle Iqbal," said Samira. "But where *is* Nani's card?"

أجابت الأم: "ربما سيأتي في دورة البريد الثانية. الآن أسرعا
وساعداني في إعداد المائدة".
"أنظر الى كل هذا الطعام!" تعجبت سميرة وقالت: "يا له من عيد!"

"Maybe it will come in the second post. Now hurry up and help me get
these dishes onto the table," said Mum.
"Look at all that food," gasped Samira. "What a feast!"

دُق جرس الباب مرات ومرات، وكانت الخالات والعمات والأعمام والجيران
يصلون. وكان هناك كثير من العناق والقبلات والضحكات والهدايا.
لم يكن حسن وسميرة يصدقا أعينهما.
وأعلن الوالد: "تفضلوا اجلسوا، الطعام جاهز".

The door bell rang, again and again, as aunts and uncles, friends and
neighbours arrived. There was hugging and kissing, laughter and presents.
Samira and Hassan could hardly believe their eyes.
"Come and sit down everyone. The food is ready," announced Dad.

قال الوالد: "اجلسي هنا يا سميرة".
فأجابت سميرة: "لكن هذا المكان خالي!"
"لم يعد خالياً" أجاب صوت مألوف.

"Samira, come and sit here," said Dad.
"But this chair's empty," said Samira, pointing to the chair next to her.
"Not for long," said a familiar voice.

"عيد مبارك لكل واحد" قالت الجدة وهي تبتسم. "لم أثق في ان ترسل المستشفى الكارت في الوقت المناسب، لذا فلم يكن أمامي إلا ان أحضره بنفسي".
ضحكت سميرة وسألت: "ولكن كيف حضرت الى هنا؟"

"Eid Mubarak everyone," said Nani, smiling. "Samira, I just couldn't trust that hospital to get the card to you on time. So what could I do but bring it myself." Samira laughed. "But how did you get here?"

"تلك قصة طويلة، ولكن أولاً هذا شيء صغير لك ولحسن"
أجابت الجدة.
وعندما فتحت سميرة وحسن الهدية وجدا بداخلها كتاباً.
ولكنه لم يكن كتاباً عادياً.
وسببت البسمة على وجههما ضحك كل الموجودين.

"That is a long story, but first, a little something for you and Hassan," said Nani.
When Samira and Hassan opened their present, they found a book inside.
But this was no ordinary book, and the smiles on their faces made eveybody laugh.

وفي آخر النهار تكورت سميرة الى جانب الجدة على "الكنبة" وهي
سعيدة، وطلب حسن من الجدة: "أحكي لنا القصة يا جدتي؟"
قالت الجدة: "كان الوقت رمضان وكان الكل صائماً، ولكن
الأطفال..."

By the end of the day, a happy Samira had curled up on the sofa next to Nani.
"Nani, tell us your story now," asked Hassan.
"Well, it was during Ramadan, when everybody was fasting, that the children
were..."

Glossary

Eid-ul Fitr

Mosque

Fasting

Muslim

Imam

Ramadan

Islam

Shalwar Kameez

Mecca

Zakat

record   stop   play

Kosovo

Azerbaijan

Turkey

Syria

Lebanon

Iraq

Tunisia

Jordan

Kuwait

Morocco

Bahrai

Qatar

Algeria

Egypt

Saudi Arabia

Libya

Mauritania

Mali

Niger

Chad

Sudan

Eritrea

Yemen

Senegal

Djbouti

The Gambia

Burkina
Faso

Guinea

Nigeria

Somalia

Sierra
Leone

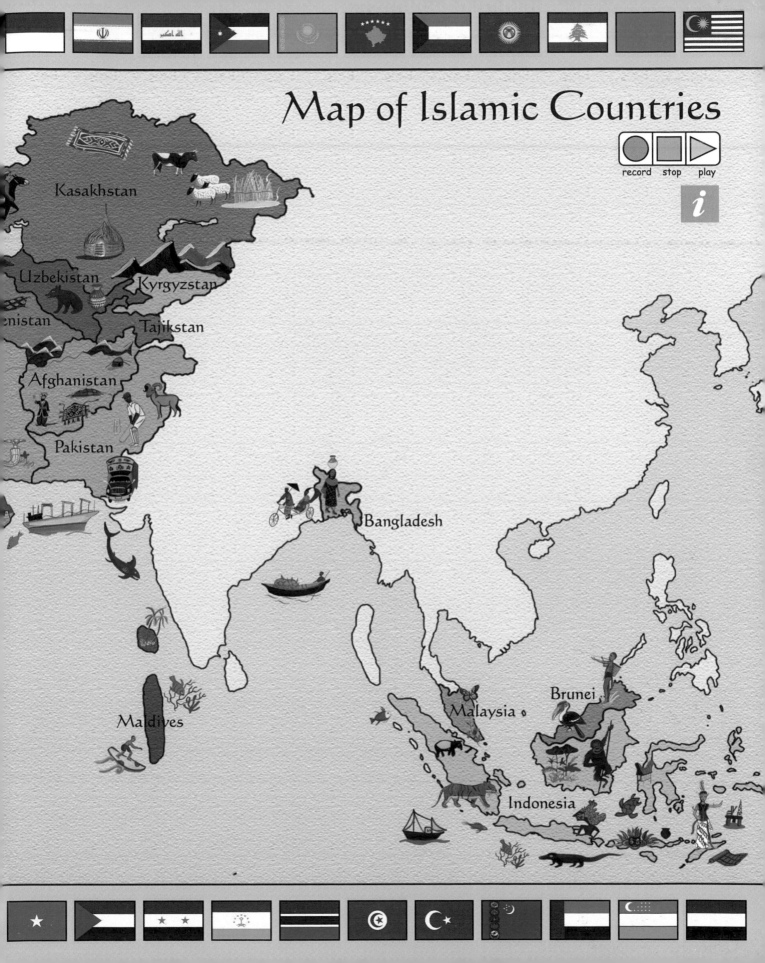

Map of Islamic Countries

record stop play

Kasakhstan

Uzbekistan Kyrgyzstan

enistan Tajikstan

Afghanistan

Pakistan

Bangladesh

Maldives

Malaysia Brunei

Indonesia

Tessellations in Islamic Art

It is believed in many Islamic cultures that art should reflect the meaning and essence of life, rather than physical appearance, which is why people and animals are not represented in places of worship. Instead, Islamic art tends to feature abstract patterns from nature, tessellations and calligraphy. Tessellations are endless repeating shapes which fit together to form a pattern. Because they can go on forever, it is said that they can help people to meditate on the infinite nature of existence.

You can experiment with designs by putting shapes together in different ways.

Tessellations can be simple or very intricate. The examples below seem complicated but if you look closely you can see that they have been made up of a few simple shapes.

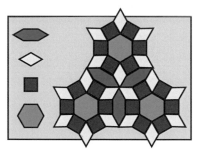 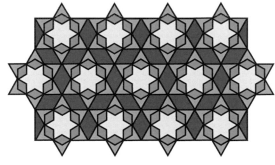 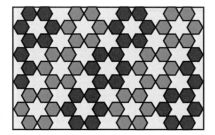

This pattern is just a series of hexagons, but because they overlap, diamonds and stars and other shapes are created. Within each of these smaller shapes, little designs have been drawn to make the pattern seem very intricate. Why not make your own pattern using this method.

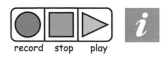
record   stop   play

i

Activities

Can you see these individual shapes in the patterns?

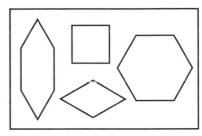

Trace over the shapes in the box lots of times and cut them out. Can you put them together in a pattern without leaving any gaps?

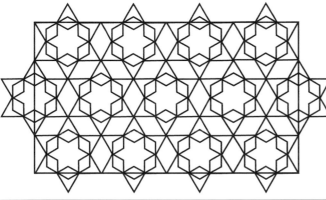
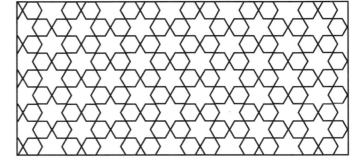

Making Eid Cards

At the beginning of the story, Samira and Hassan write cards to friends and relatives to wish them a Happy Eid. In return, they receive cards wishing them the very same. Eid cards are typically highly decorated and colourful. The more colour the better!

Folding card

i

Folding paper

Happy Eid

Eid mubarak

record   stop   play

Why not make your own Eid cards for your friends? Here are some examples that you can photocopy. You can colour them in and add your own designs and greetings.

Eid is celebrated all over the world. Below are some greetings in different languages that you can use in your card:

Eid Mubarak

Happy Eid
English

جێژنەتان پیرۆز
Kurdish

عید مبارک
Farsi

عيد مبارك
Arabic

عیدمبارک
Urdu

Ciid Wanaagsan
Somali

ঈদ মুবারক
Bengali

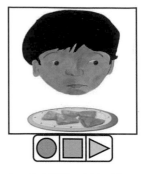

Eid Quiz! i

1. What is the name of the month during which Muslims fast?

2. What does it mean when the new moon is sighted?

3. For how long do Samira and Hassan fast?

4. What is zakat?

5. What did everyone go to the mosque to do?

6. What was the present that Nani gave to Samira and Hassan?

7. Why are tessellations commonly used in islamic art and what do they represent?

8. Name five predominantly Islamic countries.

9. What greeting might you put on an Eid card?

10. What is the holiest place for Muslims?

Traditional Food

Sfouf is a Lebanese sweet traditionally served with tea or milk. It is easy to make and delicious! Why not have a go?

Preparation time: about 10 minutes
Cooking time: 30-35 minutes
Oven temperature: 180° C (350° F)

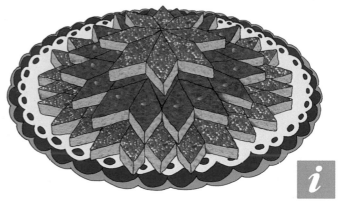

Ingredients:

750 ml semolina
560 ml sugar
500 ml milk
250 ml plain flour
250 ml vegetable oil

60 ml tahini (sesame paste)
1 teaspoon baking powder
1 teaspoon turmeric
125 ml pine nuts or almonds

Method

1. Put the semolina, flour, turmeric and baking powder into a mixing bowl. Stir well to combine the ingredients.
2. Dissolve the sugar in the milk. Then add the milk, sugar and vegetable oil to the dry ingredients and stir.
3. If you like you can spread the tahini over the base and sides of a 40cm baking tray.
4. Slowly pour the batter into the tray. Sprinkle with pine nuts or slivers of almonds.
5. Place in a preheated oven at 180° C (350° F) and bake for 30-35 minutes or until the batter is golden brown.
6. Remove from the oven and cool for 15-20 minutes. Cut either into squares or diamond shapes.

Facts about samosas

Samosas are small triangles of filled pastry. It is believed that they originate from Central Asia, and spread far and wide because they were great for long journeys. Travellers could make them over camp fires and pack them into saddle bags for the day ahead. There are many different ways of making samosas - they can have all kinds of herbs, vegetables and spices. Here are some ingredients commonly used:

Vegetables: Potatoes, peas, onion, cabbage, pumpkin, mushrooms, tomatoes, cauliflower, carrot
Meat: Minced lamb, minced beef
Herbs and spices: Red & green chilli, ginger, coriander, garam masala, salt, pepper, fennel powder, cumin seeds, mustard seeds, garlic, cardamom, mint leaves
Other: Cashew nuts, paneer, raisins, mango powder
Pastry: Samosas are usually fried, but some people prefer to bake them as this is more healthy. Filo pastry is better for frying, and puff pastry is better for baking. There are many ways of folding the pastry. Here are a couple of examples:

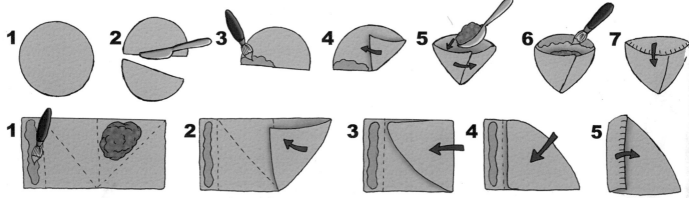